HIGHLANDERS

Photographs
Laurie Campbell

Text
Alan Edwards

Castor & Pollux

Nowadays we call them 'Highlanders', a fitting name for the ancient breed of cattle that has survived for longer than anyone can tell on the windswept moors and rugged hills of the Scottish Highlands and Islands. Originally they were known as "the black cattle" or "Kyloes" - black because that was their predominant colour, and Kyloes after the "kyles" or narrow sea straits the island herds were swum or ferried across on their long treks to the lowland cattle markets. In 1824, a visitor to the Western Isles recorded the scene on Islay where the cattle in their hundreds waited to be ferried to the neighbouring island of Jura and thence to the mainland: "The shore was covered with cattle; while the noise of the drovers and the boatmen, and all the bustle and vociferation which whisky did not tend to diminish, were re-echoed from hill to hill."

On the remote croftlands where these West Highland cattle were bred the soil was too poor to provide much winter-feeding for livestock, and each year surplus animals were taken to be sold and then fattened on the rich lowland pastures of southern Scotland and northern England. The journey was hard, and no other breed could have undertaken it; setting off in late summer with the sun on their backs and hoping to arrive at the great "trysts" or markets at Crieff, Stirling, Falkirk or beyond before winter had set in and their route became impassable. It was only with the coming of the railways and steamships in the mid nineteenth century that this annual odyssey — a central feature of Scottish rural life for some three hundred years — was finally consigned to the history books.

The black cattle were not especially big, but what they lacked in size they more than made up for in strength and stamina. They could walk extraordinary distances on their short, sturdy legs, untroubled by the rocky ground, steep ascents, driving rain or the early snow flurries that swept through the mountain passes as they followed the well-trodden drove roads south. They were accompanied by the drovers — Highlanders too, and a race of men as hardy and resilient as the beasts in their charge.

The drovers were paid little and lived sparingly on oats, onions, and ewe's milk cheese, sleeping beneath the stars and keeping the cold at bay with the whisky in their ram's-horn flasks. Sometimes they would augment their meagre rations by bleeding one of the cattle and mixing the blood with oats to produce a type of black pudding.

They drove the herds on foot, cajoling, chasing, wielding the stick, and calling out to them in their native Gaelic tongue. They would cover perhaps ten miles in a day, stopping only where they found enough good grass for the cattle to graze. As they progressed they would meet and join with clansmen from other islands or the far northern counties, and the size of the herds would swell, adding to the general commotion and excitement. What a spectacle it must have been as the cattle in their thousands finally drew near to the market towns; the drovers, weary and dishevelled in their rough Highland plaid, accompanying these wild-looking beasts with their shaggy coats and ferocious horns.

Perhaps some witnesses to this annual invasion from beyond the mountains believed these cattle to be truly wild animals, so different were they in looks and temperament from the short-haired breeds that traditionally grazed their own lowland pastures. And even today the precise origin of these primitive, almost mammoth-like creatures remains a mystery. Some believe them to be directly descended from Bos primigenius, the auroch or European wild ox, which roamed Scotland's forests and grasslands from the last Ice Age until the species became extinct around the ninth century. Others maintain that the breed was derived from a previously domesticated strain of cattle, possibly of Asiatic origin, which was introduced to northern Britain by the first humans settlers 5000 years ago. It is even possible that at one time the auroch and domesticated cattle co-existed and interbred in some remote parts of the Highlands, but in the end we are forced to admit that we are confronted by a riddle that has yet to be solved.

What is certain is that the breed still demonstrates primitive traits absent in other domesticated strains. Highland bulls, for example, keep a close watch over their herds, leading them carefully across rain-swollen rivers or marshy ground, while the normally placid cows become unusually protective of their newly born calves, concealing them in undergrowth or thick vegetation until they are able to run freely. The cow will only return once or twice a day to suckle the calf, and although she might be grazing as much as a mile away, the youngster, like the young of the wild red deer, will remain quietly in its hiding place.

These primitive instincts suggest that the breed has been changed very little over the centuries, and there were sound practical reasons for this. In 1578 Bishop Leslie compared the cattle on the islands to the wild deer "which through certain wildness of nature, flee the company or sight of men". While this may no longer be entirely true, the crofters always understood the need to preserve a certain "wildness" in their cattle, as a passage written by an islander almost 200 years ago illustrates : "Strangers, on visiting the Western Isles, cry out against the folly of the people in keeping cattle of a small breed; when by changing it for the Irish, or the Lowland Scotch, they might greatly enlarge the carcasses of their stock. But this is often a rash opinion ... Heavy cattle cannot seek their food in bogs and marshes, leap over ravines, rivers, and ditches, or scramble through rocks, and in the faces of cliffs and precipices, like the present breed, which is almost as active and nimble as a Chamois; nor can the Hebridean tenant afford to breed any stock which is not proof against the inclemency of his rains and storms all the year round."

Today's Highlander can still scramble through rocks and withstand fierce North Atlantic gales, but it does differ from its forbears in some respects, notably in the colour of the coat and in size. At one time the breed was divided into two classes : the small, dark Kyloe from the Western Isles and the larger, lighter coloured Highlander from the mainland.

In 885, a year after the Scottish Highland Cattle Society was formed, most of the pedigree bulls registered in the Society's first Herd Book were black — dark animals being considered hardier than light ones. However, by 1919 the situation was reversed and we learn that lighter coloured animals — red-brindles, light reds, yellows, and silver-duns — were preferred, and that black bulls could scarcely be sold.

Of course, during most of the breed's long history the colouring of the coat was of little consequence; the cattle's importance was as a source of meat, milk, hides and yarn for the families that eked a living on the remote island crofts. But as their value increased, and more and more animals were exported each year, the size of the herds grew and more attention was paid to breeding. By the early nineteenth century there were about 150,000 cattle in the Western Isles, as well as substantial numbers in the Highlands and the Northern Isles of Orkney and Shetland. By then large herds (or "folds" as they are properly known) had been established throughout the region, and the finest of these folds, such as those on the islands of Uist and Barra, were regarded as mainstays of the breed, preserving the unique qualities for which it had always been valued.

One of the oldest and most famous mainland folds, from which all the principal breeders in Scotland were once said to have obtained their best blood, was at Glenlyon in Perthshire. These cattle were typical Highlanders, larger and lighter in colour than the West Highland Kyloes, and the movement of prize bulls from this and other mainland herds to islands such as Harris and Skye in the nineteenth century would certainly have altered the colouring and size of the island cattle, breaking down the old distinction between Kyloe and Highlander and forming the basis of the breed as we know it today.

Highland cattle breeders took enormous pride in their stock, gathering at the annual spring shows in Oban to exhibit and sell their prize animals, but farming in Scotland was changing and soon people were questioning whether there was a place in the modern world for such an old-fashioned animal, a relic of the past which was both slower to mature and yielded less beef than other breeds. By the dawn of the twentieth century the Highlander's heyday had passed and it seemed that this "breed of great antiquity", as the early Herd Books described it, was destined to become no more than a curiosity. The Highlander, however, possessed a quality which no other breed could match, and which would prove its salvation — its looks.

The nineteenth century was a time of sweeping changes throughout the Highlands and Islands. The catalyst was the defeat of the Jacobite army at Culloden in 1746, and the infamous Highland Clearances which followed in its wake destroyed the social fabric of the entire region. The clan system was dismantled and thousands of crofters were driven from the land. The cattle were gradually replaced by more profitable sheep as wealthy English farmers moved their flocks onto the vacant grazing, and a way of life that had survived for centuries was lost forever. Inevitably a nostalgia for this vanished past was felt, and it found expression in the historical novels of Sir Walter Scott. The widespread popularity of Scott's writings began to lure wealthy travellers to the Highlands in search of a land steeped in romance and populated by a race of noble clansmen. Suddenly the Highlands were fashionable, and they became even more so when, in 1848, Queen Victoria bought Balmoral Castle in Deeside as her country residence.

It was the beginning of the mythologising of the Highlands, and if any creature embodied the spirit of this mythical land it was the Highlander. Pictured by artists gazing sternly out through the mist, with finely tapered horns and his long coat rippling in the breeze, he presented an irresistible image — as wild as the rushing river and as ancient as the mountains in whose shadow he grazed. It was not long before every self-respecting Highland Laird kept a few pure-bred Highlanders simply as a means of decorating his grounds and impressing his guests.

Understandably, no one wanted to alter the appearance of such an exotic specimen, and typical characteristics of a thick coat, short sturdy legs and long well-proportioned body have survived intact to this day. Not only that, today's pure-bred Highlander is every bit as hardy as the tough little Kyloe of years gone by. But while the tourists that flock to the Highlands continue to be delighted and astonished by the animal's striking appearance, its practical value is gradually being rediscovered too.

The Highlander's unique ability to convert even the poorest pastures into quality beef, allied to a growing demand for organic meat, is now working in its favour. These cattle, like the red deer, store their fat internally around the kidneys, and the beef they produce is exceptionally lean. It has a superb flavour too, as was recognised long ago when the herds were taken south to be fattened and butchered for the English market. The breed's legendary hardiness and adaptability are also being exploited in other parts of the world. They have been introduced to nature reserves in the Netherlands, where they now live in a semi-wild state amid the heather and birch trees, keeping the vegetation under control and conserving the land. Similarly, high in the Austrian Alps they have restored the natural balance to pastures which were suffering from soil erosion because the summer vegetation was no longer being grazed.

The breed's popularity shows no sign of diminishing either. New folds are constantly being established and membership of the Highland Cattle Society continues to grow. Highlanders are now found throughout the British Isles, and are once more roaming the wild moors and summer flower meadows of their ancestral home in the Western Isles. Denmark, Germany, Canada, America and Australia are among the countries that have successfully imported Highland cattle, and many now have their own national Societies. It is even reported that Highlanders can be found grazing 10,000 feet up in the South American Andes.

The face of the Highlands may have changed since the days of the ancient drove roads, and the high mountain passes will never again resound to the shouts of the drovers and the lowing of the black cattle, but the Highlander's future at last seems secure. And this is as it should be, because he really is a mythic beast, a mysterious creature in whose striking form and inscrutable gaze the long history of a land and its people is somehow distilled.

First published in France
in 2000 by Castor & Pollux Edition
Tel. 33 (0)3 25 03 03 30

ISBN : 2-912756-42-1
Printed in France by Néo Typo in Besançon
Graphic Design Atelier **Hit**OrMiss - Paris
Editions Castor & Pollux - 52190 Chassigny